Can You Car

Here is a bee,
all yellow and black,
with four little wings
upon its back.
Can you carry it, Harriet?

2

Here is a puddle
to splash and splosh in,
good for giving your shoes
a wash in.
Can you carry it, Harriet?

4

5

Here is a nest
of straw on the floor,
with warm, brown eggs,
1, 2, 3, 4.
Can you carry it, Harriet?

Here comes Harriet's
good friend Sue.
Let's ask her
what we can do.

8

9

Scoop the puddle up in a bucket.
Now you can carry it, Harriet.

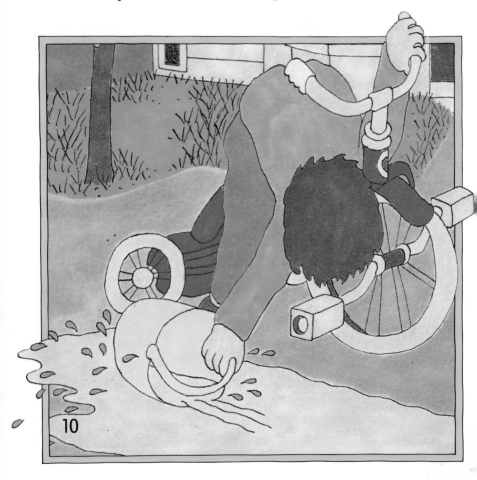

Catch the bee in a little jar.
Now you can carry it, Harriet.

Put the nest of eggs in a basket.
Now you can carry it, Harriet.

Take the bucket
and water the plants.

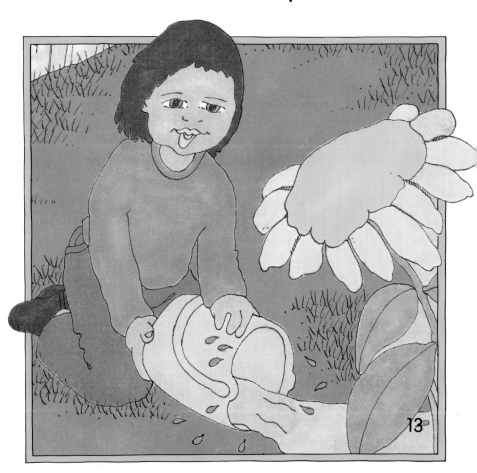

Open the jar and free the bee.

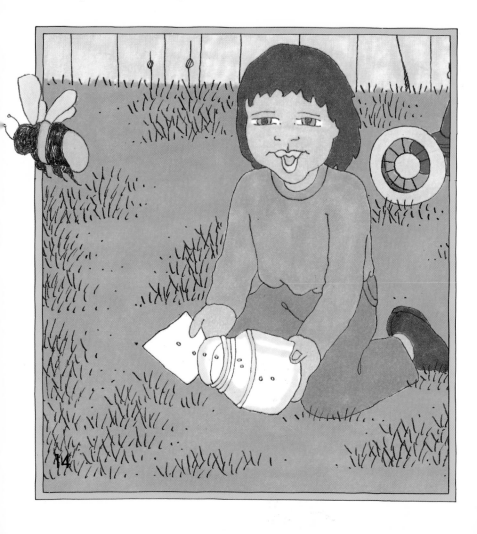

Take just one egg carefully.

Yes, you can carry it, Harriet.